IMAGINE THAT

Licensed exclusively to Imagine That Publishing Ltd
Tide Mill Way, Woodbridge, Suffolk, IP12 1AP, UK
www.imaginethat.com
Copyright © 2021 Imagine That Group Ltd
All rights reserved
2 4 6 8 9 7 5 3 1
Manufactured in China

Written by Seb Davey
Illustrated by Julia Seal

ISBN 978-1-80105-353-2

A catalogue record for this book is available from the British Library

Bear's Little Book of
Calm

Written by
Seb Davey

Illustrated by
Julia Seal

Breathe. Count 1.

Calm.

Be still ...

It's good to take
things slow sometimes.

Breathe. Count 2.

Listen.

Really listen ...

What can
you hear?

Breathe. Count 3.

Look.

Notice things ...

What can you see?

Breathe. Count 4.

Feel.

Step outside ...

Feel the air on your skin.

Breathe. Count 5. **Hug.**

You're not alone ...

Enjoy the warmth of being together.

Breathe. Count 6.

Eat.

Take your time ...

Taste and appreciate every flavour.

Breathe. Count 7.

Talk.

Be open and honest ...

Share feelings
with yourself
and others.

Breathe. Count 8.

Share.

Share with your heart ...

Show your family that you
care about them.

Breathe. Count 9.

Focus.

Dream big ...

You can follow your dreams.

Breathe. Count 10.

Exercise.

Clear your thoughts ...

Enjoy and notice your surroundings.

Breathe.
Count 11.

Be quiet.

Listen to the sound
of your heart ...

Let everything else
drift away.

Breathe. Count 12.

Smile.

Be happy in the moment ...

Remember the good things about your day.

Calm.

Listen.

Look.

Feel.

Hug.

Eat.

Talk.

Share.

Focus.

Exercise.

Be quiet.

Smile.